The Walrus and the Carpenter

This book was compiled by Sarah Cure (15.08.67-19.08.09)
who sadly passed away aged 42 before it was published.
It is dedicated to all her family.

First published 2009
by Walker Books Ltd
87 Vauxhall Walk,
London SE11 5HJ

10 9 8 7 6 5 4 3 2 1

Text © 2009 individual authors
as noted in the acknowledgements

Cover illustration © 2009 Quentin Blake

This book has been typeset in Frutiger

Printed and bound in Great Britain
by Clays Ltd, St Ives plc

British Library Cataloguing in Publication Data:
a catalogue record for this book is available
from the British Library

ISBN 978-1-4063-2650-5

www.walker.co.uk

The Walrus and the Carpenter

and other favourite poems in aid of The Children's Trust

WALKER BOOKS
AND SUBSIDIARIES
LONDON · BOSTON · SYDNEY · AUCKLAND

Contents

Carol Ann Duffy was born in Glasgow. She grew up
in Stafford and then attended the University of Liverpool,
where she studied Philosophy. She has written for
both children and adults, and her poetry has received many
awards, including the *Signal Prize for Children's Verse*,
the *Whitbread* and *Forward* prizes, as well as the
Lannan Award and the *E. M. Forster Prize* in America.
Carol Ann Duffy was made Poet Laureate in 2009.

Foreword

You hold in your hands a lovely, vibrant
anthology of poems for children chosen by an
exciting and popular range of people – from
Jacqueline Wilson via McFly to Paul O'Grady,
with rugby players and actors in-between.
All of these people share a common belief –
that poetry is important for the young reader
and that poetry is special – funny, strange,
moving, memorable – an event in language.
They've all selected poems that *they* remember;
that are distinctive enough for them to want to
share and celebrate. From Lewis Carroll and
Edward Lear to the perennially popular
Roger McGough, the poems here dance
their word play across the pages and into
the head and heart. A poem is unique
in that once it truly enters your mind, it
will never leave you and I hope that young
readers will find a poem here that will
stay with them forever. Enjoy!

Carol Ann Duffy
Poet Laureate

Eletelephony

By Laura Elizabeth Richards

Once there was an elephant,
Who tried to use the telephant—
No! no! I mean an elephone
Who tried to use the telephone—
(Dear me! I am not certain quite
That even now I've got it right.)

Howe'er it was, he got his trunk
Entangled in the telephunk;
The more he tried to get it free,
The louder buzzed the telephee—
(I fear I'd better drop the song
Of elephop and telephong!)

Selected by Henry Winkler,
actor, producer, children's author

The Owl and the Pussy-Cat

By Edward Lear

The Owl and the Pussy-Cat went to sea
In a beautiful pea-green boat.
They took some honey, and plenty of money
Wrapped up in a five pound-note.
The Owl looked up to the stars above,
And sang to a small guitar,
"O lovely Pussy! O Pussy, my love,
What a beautiful Pussy you are,
You are,
You are!
What a beautiful Pussy you are."

Pussy said to the Owl, "You elegant fowl!
How charmingly sweet you sing!
O let us be married, too long have we tarried:
But what shall we do for a ring?"
They sailed away, for a year and a day,
To the land where the Bong-Tree grows,
And there in a wood a Piggy-wig stood,
With a ring at the end of his nose,
His nose,
His nose!
With a ring at the end of his nose.

"Dear Pig, are you willing, to sell for one shilling
Your ring?" Said the Piggy, "I will."
So they took it away, and were married next day
By the Turkey who lives on the hill.
They dined on mince, and slices of quince,
Which they ate with a runcible spoon;
And hand in hand, on the edge of the sand
They danced by the light of the moon,
The moon,
The moon,
They danced by the light of the moon.

Selected by McFly, popular british band

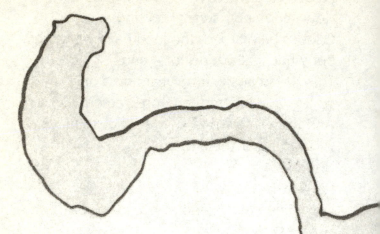

Farewell, Pete

By Roger Stevens

I had a little dinosaur
Nothing would it eat
But a chocolate cupcake
And my best mate, Pete

At school it burst the football
It wasn't fond of sports
It gobbled up the goalposts
and Mr Walton's shorts

It chased my Auntie Emma
You should have heard her shout
But it didn't like my granny
In fact, it spat her out

Selected by Michael Absalom, TV presenter

The Walrus and the Carpenter

By Lewis Carroll

The sun was shining on the sea,
Shining with all his might:
He did his very best to make
The billows smooth and bright –
And this was odd, because it was
The middle of the night.

The moon was shining sulkily,
Because she thought the sun
Had got no business to be there
After the day was done –
"It's very rude of him," she said,
"To come and spoil the fun!"

The sea was wet as wet could be,
The sands were dry as dry.
You could not see a cloud, because
No cloud was in the sky:
No birds were flying overhead –
There were no birds to fly.

The Walrus and the Carpenter
Were walking close at hand:
They wept like anything to see
Such quantities of sand:
"If this were only cleared away,"
They said, "it *would* be grand!"

"If seven maids with seven mops
Swept it for half a year,
Do you suppose," the Walrus said,
"That they could get it clear?"
"I doubt it," said the Carpenter,
And shed a bitter tear.

"O Oysters, come and walk with us!"
The Walrus did beseech.
"A pleasant walk, a pleasant talk,
Along the briny beach:
We cannot do with more than four,
To give a hand to each."

The eldest Oyster looked at him,
But never a word he said:
The eldest Oyster winked his eye,
And shook his heavy head –
Meaning to say he did not choose
To leave the oyster-bed.

But four young Oysters hurried up,
All eager for the treat:
Their coats were brushed, their faces washed,
Their shoes were clean and neat –
And this was odd, because, you know,
They hadn't any feet.

Four other Oysters followed them,
And yet another four;
And thick and fast they came at last,
And more, and more, and more –
All hopping through the frothy waves,
And scrambling to the shore.

The Walrus and the Carpenter
Walked on a mile or so,
And then they rested on a rock
Conveniently low:
And all the little Oysters stood
And waited in a row.

"The time has come," the Walrus said,
"To talk of many things:
Of shoes – and ships – and sealing-wax –
Of cabbages – and kings –
And why the sea is boiling hot –
And whether pigs have wings."

"But wait a bit," the Oysters cried,
"Before we have our chat;
For some of us are out of breath,
And all of us are fat!"
"No hurry!" said the Carpenter.
They thanked him much for that.

"A loaf of bread," the Walrus said,
"Is what we chiefly need:
Pepper and vinegar besides
Are very good indeed –
Now if you're ready, Oysters dear,
We can begin to feed."

"But not on us!" the Oysters cried,
Turning a little blue.
"After such kindness, that would be
A dismal thing to do!"
"The night is fine," the Walrus said.
"Do you admire the view?

"It was so kind of you to come!
And you are very nice!"
The Carpenter said nothing but
"Cut us another slice!
I wish you were not quite so deaf –
I've had to ask you twice!"

"It seems a shame," the Walrus said,
"To play them such a trick,
After we've brought them out so far,
And made them trot so quick!"
The Carpenter said nothing but
"The butter's spread too thick!"

"I weep for you," the Walrus said:
"I deeply sympathize."
With sobs and tears he sorted out
Those of the largest size,
Holding his pocket-handkerchief
Before his streaming eyes.

"O Oysters," said the Carpenter,
"You've had a pleasant run!
Shall we be trotting home again?'
But answer came there none –
And this was scarcely odd, because
They'd eaten every one.

**Selected by Quentin Blake, CBE,
illustrator and former Children's Laureate**

21

First Day at School

By Roger McGough

A millionbillionwillion miles from home
Waiting for the bell to go. (To go where?)
Why are they all so big, other children?
So noisy? So much at home they
Must have been born in uniform
Lived all their lives in playgrounds.
Spent the years inventing games
that don't let me in. Games
that are rough, that swallow you up.

And the railings.
All around, the railings.
Are they to keep out wolves and monsters?
Things that carry off and eat children?
Things you don't take sweets from?
Perhaps they're to stop us getting out.
Running away from the lessins. Lessin.
What does a lessin look like?
Sounds small and slimy.
They keep them in glassrooms.
Whole rooms made out of glass. Imagine.

Selected by Andrew Castle, TV presenter

I wish I could remember my name.
Mummy said it would come in useful.
Like wellies. When there's puddles.
Yellowwellies. I wish she was here.
I think my name is sewn on somewhere.
Perhaps the teacher will read it for me.
Tea-cher. The one who makes the tea.

Two Little Kittens

By Jane Taylor

Two little kittens
One stormy night,
Began to quarrel,
And then to fight.

One had a mouse
And the other had none;
And that was the way
The quarrel begun.

"I'll have that mouse,"
Said the bigger cat.
"You'll have that mouse?
We'll see about that!"

"I will have that mouse"
Said the tortoise-shell;
And, spitting and scratching,
On her sister she fell.

I've told you before
'Twas a stormy night
When these two little kittens
Began to fight.

The old woman took
The sweeping broom,
And swept them both
Right out of the room.

The ground was covered
With frost and snow,
They had lost the mouse,
And had nowhere to go.

So they lay and shivered
Beside the door,
Till the old woman finished
Sweeping the floor.

And then they crept in
As quiet as mice,
All wet with snow
And as cold as ice.

They found it much better
That stormy night,
To lie by the fire,
Than to quarrel and fight.

**Selected by Rebecca Romero, MBE,
Olympic medallist**

Somewhere I have Never Travelled, Gladly Beyond

By e.e. cummings

somewhere i have never travelled,gladly beyond
any experience,your eyes have their silence:
in your most frail gesture are things which enclose me,
or which i cannot touch because they are too near

your slightest look easily will unclose me
though i have closed myself as fingers,
you open always petal by petal myself as Spring opens
(touching skilfully,mysteriously)her first rose

or if your wish be to close me,i and
my life will shut very beautifully,suddenly,
as when the heart of this flower imagines
the snow carefully everywhere descending;

nothing which we are to perceive in this world equals
the power of your intense fragility:whose texture
compels me with the colour of its countries,
rendering death and forever with each breathing

(i do not know what it is about you that closes
and opens;only something in me understands
the voice of your eyes is deeper than all roses)
nobody,not even the rain,has such small hands

Selected by Sienna Miller, actress

The Hamster's Revenge

By Paul Cookson

No one realised, nobody knew
The hamster was sleeping inside my dad's shoe.

He put in his foot and squashed flat his nose
So it opened its jaws and chomped on his toes.

While howling and yowling and hopping like mad
The hamster wreaked further revenge on my dad.

It scampered and scurried up his trouser leg
And this time bit something much softer instead.

His eyes bulged and popped like marbles on stalks
And watered while walking the strangest of walks.

His ears wiggled wildly while shooting out steam
All the dogs in the town heard his falsetto scream.

His face went deep purple, his hair stood on end,
His mouth like a letter box caught in the wind.

The hamster's revenge was almost complete...
Dad couldn't sit down for seventeen weeks.

Now dad doesn't give the hamster a chance...
He wears stainless-steel socks and hamster-proof pants.

Selected by Simon Shaw, MBE,
England international rugby player

Barbecue

By Francesca Major (aged 10)

The animals came in two by two.
They all queued up for the barbecue.
"How do you do?" said the elder ewe.
"What's all the hullabaloo?" said the smelly kangaroo.
"Nothing to do with you!" said the sizzling burgers
On the barbecue!

Winner of *The Children's Trust* Poetry Competition 2009

The Cricket Field

By Arthur Salway

Fortunate indeed this field;
It's destiny is not to yield
A harvest made with wheat and corn
From rutting plough or harrow born,
But cleared of lump and stump and thicket
Is set aside for playing cricket.

In winter gentle sheep may graze
Preserving turf for summer days,
A picket fence thrown round the square
Should hoof or human trespass there.
Some say we should share—use the land:
Clearly, they don't understand.

This field shall always take its name
Only from England's noblest game.
Despite its level disposition
And most favourable condition
Hockey posts shall not be found,
This is no recreation ground.

Four generations, maybe more,
Since long before the first World War,
Cricketers long gone, and some
Who play today, and those to come,
All sow unmixed the seeds of cricket
And harvest only run and wicket.

Selected by Phil Tufnell,
TV personality, former England cricketer
and Vice-President of *The Children's Trust*

Story of Little Suck-a Thumb

from *Struwwelpeter*
by Heinrich Hoffman

One day Mamma said "Conrad dear,
I must go out and leave you here.
But mind now, Conrad, what I say,
Don't suck your thumb while I'm away.
The great tall tailor always comes
To little boys who suck their thumbs;
And ere they dream what he's about,
He takes his great sharp scissors out,
And cuts their thumbs clean off – and then,
You know, they never grow again."

Mamma had scarcely turned her back,
The thumb was in, Alack! Alack!
The door flew open, in he ran,
The great, long, blue-legged scissor-man.
Oh! children, see! the tailor's come
And caught out little Suck-a-Thumb.

Snip!
Snap!
Snip!

the scissors go;
And Conrad cries out "Oh! Oh! Oh!"

Snip!
Snap!
Snip!

They go so fast,
That both his thumbs are off at last.

Mamma comes home: there Conrad stands,
And looks quite sad, and shows his hands;
"Ah!" said Mamma, "I knew he'd come
To naughty little Suck-a-Thumb."

Selected by Lorraine Kelly, TV presenter

Old Noah's Ark

By Anon

Old Noah once he built an ark,
And patched it up with hickory bark.
He anchored it to a great big rock,
And then he began to load his stock.

The animals went in one by one,
The elephant chewing a carroway bun.

The animals went in two by two,
The crocodile and the kangaroo.

The animals went in three by three,
The tall giraffe and the tiny flea.

The animals went in four by four,
The hippopotamus stuck in the door.

The animals went in five by five,
The bees mistook the bear for a hive.

The animals went in six by six,
The monkey was up to his usual tricks.

The animals went in seven by seven,
Said the ant to the elephant, "Who're ye shoving?"

The animals went in eight by eight,
Some were early and some were late.

The animals went in nine by nine,
They all formed fours and marched in line.

The animals went in ten by ten,
If you want any more, you can read it again!

**Selected by Vic Reeves, comedian and
Nancy Sorrell, model, actress and TV presenter**

Disobedience

By A.A. Milne

James James
Morrison Morrison
Weatherby George Dupree
Took great
Care of his Mother,
Though he was only three.
James James
Said to his Mother,
"Mother," he said, said he:
"You must never go down to the end of the town,
if you don't go down with me."

James James
Morrison's Mother
Put on a golden gown,
James James
Morrison's Mother
Drove to the end of the town.
James James
Morrison's Mother
Said to herself, said she:
"I can get right down to the end of the town
and be back in time for tea."

King John
Put up a notice,

"LOST or STOLEN or STRAYED!

JAMES JAMES

MORRISON'S MOTHER

SEEMS TO HAVE BEEN MISLAID.

LAST SEEN

WANDERING VAGUELY:

QUITE OF HER OWN ACCORD,

SHE TRIED TO GET DOWN TO

THE END OF THE TOWN—

FORTY SHILLINGS

REWARD!"

James James
Morrison Morrison
(Commonly known as Jim)
Told his
Other relations
Not to go blaming *him*.
James James
Said to his Mother,
"Mother," he said, said he:
"You must *never* go down to the end of the town
without consulting me."

James James
Morrison's mother
Hasn't been heard of since.
King John
Said he was sorry,
So did the Queen and Prince.
King John
(Somebody told me)
Said to a man he knew:
"If people go down to the end of the town, well,
what can *anyone* do?"

(Now then, very softly)
J. J.
M. M.
W. G. Du P.
Took great
C/o his M*****
Though he was only 3.
J. J.
Said to his M*****
"M*****," he said, said he:
"You-must-never-go-down-to-the-end-of-the-town-
if-you-don't-go-down-with ME!"

**Selected by Penny Smith,
TV presenter**

41

A Crocodile's Teeth

By Colin West

A crocodile's teeth are a problem,
a crocodile's teeth are a pain.
A crocodile suffers the toothache
again and again and again.

Now, getting the toothache so often,
makes crocodiles lose all their bite,
and desperate measures are called for
to bring back their lost appetite.

Thus crocodiles go to the dentist
on average, every eight years.
(Quite by chance, that's precisely how often
a dentist, somewhere, disappears.)

Colin West, children's author, illustrator and poet

Goblin Market

By Christina Rossetti

Morning and evening
Maids heard the goblins cry
"Come buy our orchard fruits,
Come buy, come buy:
Apples and quinces,
Lemons and oranges,
Plump unpecked cherries,
Melons and raspberries,
Bloom-down-cheeked peaches,
Swart-headed mulberries,
Wild free-born cranberries,
Crab-apples, dewberries,
Pine-apples, blackberries,
Apricots, strawberries; –
All ripe together
In summer weather, –
Morns that pass by,
Fair eves that fly;
Come buy, come buy:
Our grapes fresh from the vine,
Pomegranates full and fine,
Dates and sharp bullaces,
Rare pears and greengages,

Damsons and bilberries,
Taste them and try:
Currants and gooseberries,
Bright-fire-like barberries,
Figs to fill your mouth,
Citrons from the South,
Sweet to tongue and sound to eye;
Come buy, come buy."

**Selected by Jacqueline Wilson, DBE,
award-winning author and former Children's Laureate**

Today I Had a Rotten Day

By Kenn Nesbitt

Today I had a rotten day.
As I was coming in from play
I accidentally stubbed my toes
and tripped and fell and whacked my nose.
I chipped a tooth. I cut my lip.
I scraped my knee. I hurt my hip.
I pulled my shoulder, tweaked my ear,
and got a bruise upon my rear.
I banged my elbow, barked my shin.
A welt is forming on my chin.
My pencil poked me in the thigh.
I got an eyelash in my eye.
I sprained my back. I wrenched my neck.
I'm feeling like a total wreck.
So that's the last time I refuse
when teacher says to tie my shoes.

Selected by Paul O'Grady, MBE,
BAFTA-award winning comedian of TV,
radio and stage

The Cat of Cats

By William Brighty Rands

I am the cat of cats. I am
The everlasting cat!
Cunning, and old, and sleek as jam,
The everlasting cat!
I hunt the vermin in the night—
The everlasting cat!
For I see best without the light—
The everlasting cat!

**Selected by Elaine Paige, OBE,
award-winning actress, singer,
broadcaster and Vice-President
of _The Children's Trust_**

Jabberwocky

By Lewis Carroll

'Twas brillig, and the slithy toves
Did gyre and gimble in the wabe:
All mimsy were the borogoves,
And the mome raths outgrabe.

"Beware the Jabberwock, my son!
The jaws that bite, the claws that catch!
Beware the Jubjub bird, and shun
The frumious Bandersnatch!"

He took his vorpal sword in hand:
Long time the manxome foe he sought –
So rested he by the Tumtum tree,
And stood awhile in thought.

And as in uffish thought he stood,
The Jabberwock, with eyes of flame,
Came whiffling through the tulgy wood,
And burbled as it came!

One, two! One, two! and through and through
The vorpal blade went snicker-snack!
He left it dead, and with its head
He went galumphing back.

"And hast thou slain the Jabberwock?
Come to my arms, my beamish boy!
O frabjous day! Callooh! Callay!"
He chortled in his joy.

'Twas brillig, and the slithy toves
Did gyre and gimble in the wabe:
All mimsy were the borogoves,
And the mome raths outgrabe.

**Selected by Richard Hammond,
broadcaster and Vice-President
of *The Children's Trust***

On the Ning Nang Nong

By Spike Milligan

On the Ning Nang Nong
Where the Cows go Bong!
And the Monkeys all say Boo!
There's a Nong Nang Ning
Where the trees go Ping!
And the tea pots Jibber Jabber Joo.
On the Nong Ning Nang
All the mice go Clang!
And you just can't catch 'em when they do!

So it's Ning Nang Nong!
Cows go Bong!
Nong Nang Ning!
Trees go Ping!
Nong Ning Nang!
The mice go Clang!
What a noisy place to belong,
Is the Ning Nang Ning Nang Nong!!

Selected by Lucy Speed, actress

When I Grow Up

By Matt Simpson

I want to be:

A systems analyst,
A game-show panellist,
A pop star
With a guitar,
A technologist,
A psychologist,
A herpetologist,

A man who studies volcanoes
An ecologist?
No, a seismologist!

I want to be:

Something in the city,
Very pretty,
A fortune teller,
A good speller,

A radar technician,
Always out fishin',
A clever magician,
A cosmetician,
A politician,

A dress designer,
A coal miner,
A good rhymer,
A charmer,
A pig farmer,

A rock and roller,
A South Pole explorer,
A moonwalker,
A New Yorker;

I want to be:

Stinking rich,
A wicked witch,
A private eye,
An engineer,
A life peer,

A DJ
OK?
A lead singer,
A right winger
For Liverpool,
Cool!

I want to be:

Taller,
Thinner,
A lottery winner!

But if none
Of these can be
I will remain
Yours truly

ME!

**Selected by Dani Harmer,
aka Tracy Beaker, actress in
The Story of Tracy Beaker
and star of *Dani's House***

Night Writing

By Carol Ann Duffy

Only a neat margin of moonlight
there at the curtain's edge.
The room like a dark page.
I lie in bed.

Silence is ink.
The sound of my breath dips in
and out. So I begin
night writing. The stars type themselves
far out in space.

Who would guess,
to look at my sleeping face,
the rhymes and tall tales I invent?
Here be dragons; children lost
in the wood; three wishes; the wicked
and the good.

Read my lips.
The small hours are poems.
Dawn is a rubber.

**Selected by Carol Ann Duffy, CBE, playwright,
writer, and current Poet Laureate**

Dear Spider

By Angela Topping

Thanks for the invitation
to your cosy dinner for two.
I'd really love to come
but I can't think what to do.
I can't decide just what to wear
my clothes are all so fine
and I'm not certain where to find
a suitable sort of wine.
I'm not used to dining out,
it's really not my thing.
I tend to snatch my meals
when I am on the wing.
My mealtime conversation
is limited in kind.
In short I feel that
I really should decline.
It's not that I don't like you
but we are so far apart;
I can't see it working out
although you want my heart.
Yours sincerely
Fly

**Selected by Helen Skelton,
Blue Peter presenter**

Poetry Writing Tips

From Colin West, children's book author, illustrator and poet

Read, read, read!

Read lots of poems. You'll discover many different forms of poem and it can be great fun writing to a certain form, such as a limerick or haiku. Be prepared for some forms being harder to write than others!

Don't feel inspired?

Make a list of words which begin with the same letter. Play around with them so they have some sort of rhythm and sense (or nonsense) to them. You may have to add a few other words to do this. What you'll end up with is an alliterative poem or tongue twister!

Don't expect to always get it right first time.

Revise your poem after you've written it. You may feel it doesn't need to rhyme so much, or you may feel some lines are superfluous. If you're only really happy with three lines of it, maybe it was meant to be a three line poem!

An incubation period can help.

You can put aside any poems and add or take away from them at a later time. I recently finished off a poem I started way back in 1972!

You can't always write poems to order!

You may find the poem you made up at the bus stop on the way home is better than the one you tried to write in class. So carry a note book for any ideas which pop into your head unexpectedly.

Write about yourself.

Make a list of your own habits and characteristics (feel free to exaggerate!). Then make them into a poem, and remember you can be as unkind and rude about yourself as you like!

The Children's Trust

This book of favourite children's poems celebrates the 25th Anniversary of *The Children's Trust*. Since 1984 the Trust has helped thousands of severely disabled children and their families. The expert medical and nursing care, specialist education and therapy that the Trust provides enables children to live their lives to the full no matter how complex their medical needs. We help their families too and our rehabilitation service helps children who have had a severe brain injury rebuild their lives. The children helped by *The Children's Trust* face enormous challenges and often enjoying normal childhood activities can be difficult. Being read to is something every child can enjoy and children at the Trust have had fun creating the illustrations for this book.

Photograph © Richard Bloomfield *The Children's Trust*

By buying it, you are helping us to reach more children in the future, and to change even more young lives.

My thanks go to Walker Books, to all the celebrities who have contributed their favourite poems, to Quentin Blake for his illustration for the cover, to the talented children who entered our poetry competition and to two very special volunteers Sarah Cure and Amanda Litster, whose drive and hard work brought this project to life. Their determination and commitment equals that of the dedicated staff and courageous children who have made the Trust what it is today, a unique place where childhood is celebrated and children are at the heart of everything we do.

Liz Haigh-Reeve
Director of Marketing and Fundraising *The Children's Trust*

Acknowledgements

"Eletelephony" by Laura Elizabeth Richards from *Tirra Lirra* by Laura
Richards. Copyright © 1930, 1932 by Laura E. Richards; Copyright ©
renewed 1960 by Hamilton Richards. By permission of Little Brown &
Company. "Farewell, Pete" © Roger Stevens 2007 from *Why Otters
Don't Wear Socks*. Macmillan Children's Books. "First Day at School"
by Roger McGough from *In the Glassroom* (© Roger McGough 1976)
is printed by permission of United Agents (www.unitedagents.co.uk)
on behalf of Roger McGough. "somewhere i have never travelled,
gladly beyond" is reprinted from *Complete Poems 1904-1962*, by
e.e. cummings, edited by George J. Firmage, by permission of W.W.Norton
& Company. Copyright © 1991 by Trustees for the e.e. cummings Trust
and George James Firmage. "The Hamster's Revenge" by Paul Cookson
is reprinted by kind permission of the author. www.paulcooksonpoet.co.uk
"The Cricket Field"by Arthur Salway is reprinted by kind permission of the
author."Disobedience" from *When We Were Very Young* by A.A. Milne.
Text © The Trustees of the Pooh Properties 1928. Published by Egmont
UK Ltd London and used with permission. "A Crocodile's Teeth" by Colin
West from *A Crocodile's Teeth* by Colin West, published by Walker Books.
Copyright © 2007 by Colin West. By permission of Walker Books. "Today
I Had a Rotten Day" copyright © 2007 Kenn Nesbitt. All Rights Reserved.
Reprinted by kind permission of the author. From the book *Revenge of the
Lunch Ladies*. Meadowbrook Press. "When I Grow Up" by Matt Simpson
is reprinted by kind permission of the author's family. "Night Writing" by
Carol Ann Duffy from *New and Collected Poems for Children*, published by
Faber. "Dear Spider" by Angela Topping from *Read Me Out Loud* chosen
by Nick Toczek and Paul Cookson (Macmillan 2007)

Every reasonable effort has been made to trace the ownership of and/or
secure permission for the use of copyrighted material. If notified of any
omission, the publisher will gladly make the necessary correction in future
printings.

With thanks to the following children and friends of *The Children's Trust* for contributing their artwork:

Amanda, Avi, Ben, Callum, Caroline, Charlotte,
Daniel, Darryl, Elijah, Elise, Finn, Geraldine,
James, Joshua, Kim, Kitty, Louise, Lynn,
Megan, Rizwan, Rose, Sara, Shanice and William.

The Children's Trust is a registered charity,
registration No: 288018